Tips for Talking and Reading Together

Read at Home *Floppy's Phonics* stories are a fun and motivating way of using letter sounds to practise reading.

- Talk about the title and the picture on the cover.
- Identify the letter patterns *ie* and *i-e* and talk about the sounds (phonemes) they make when you read them (*igh*).
- Look at the *ie* and *i-e* words on page 4. Say each word and then say the sounds in each word (e.g. *f-r-ie-d, r-i-ce*).
- Read the story and find the words with *ie* and *i-e*.
- Discuss the Talk About ideas on page 21.
- Do the fun activity at the end of the book.

Have fun!

Egg
Fried Rice

Written by Roderick Hunt

Illustrated by Nick Schon,
based on the original characters
created by Alex Brychta

OXFORD

UNIVERSITY PRESS

Read these words

fried	rice
tried	nine
cried	invite
nice	smiled

4

"I will be nine on Friday," said
Wilma. "I'd like to eat out."

"I'd like a Chinese meal," Wilma said, "and can we invite Biff and Chip?"

"That's fine," said Mum.

It was time for the Chinese meal.
They went to the Bright Sky.

"What is it like to be nine?" said
Chip. Wilma smiled.

"It's all right," she said.

"What do you like best?"
said Dad.

"I like egg fried rice," said
Wilma, "and I'll try tiger prawns."

Then all the lights went out.
Oh no. There was a fire.

"The kitchen is on fire," said
Mr Lee.

They had to go outside.
Fire-fighters came to put the
fire out.

"I am sorry," said Mr Lee.
"We must shut for the night."

Wilma was upset. She tried not to, but she cried.

"It is sad to see Wilma cry," said
Mr Lee. "Come back on Sunday
night."

On Sunday, Mr Lee put on a feast.

"Smile," said Mr Lee.

"This is so kind," said Mum.

"I had my egg fried rice," said
Wilma, "and such a nice time."

Talk about the story

Where did the family go for their meal?

What did Wilma like to eat?

Why was Wilma upset when there was a fire?

What do you like to eat when you go out for a meal?

ie, *i-e* or *igh*?

Choose the letters to make each word.

n____t   n__n__   sm__l__

tr____d   l__k__   r____t

br____t   fr____d   t__m__

More books for you to enjoy

Have more fun
with Read at Home

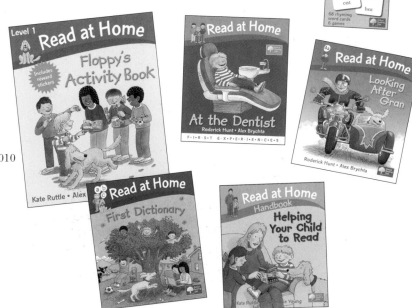

OXFORD
UNIVERSITY PRESS
Great Clarendon Street,
Oxford OX2 6DP

Text © Roderick Hunt 2009
Illustrations © Nick Schon and
Alex Brychta 2009

British Library Cataloguing
in Publication Data available

ISBN: 9780198387671

10 9 8 7 6 5 4 3 2 1

Printed in China by Imago